SOPHIE REILLY (1995 - 2016) grew
Glasgow, where she began writing poetr
childhood. A blissful infant – a happy (if   ̗ᴘᴉᴉᴇ's
earliest writings, before she had reached ter   ̪ᴜ̣ᴜ, nonetheless
speak to a sense of estrangement, of an inability to be at home
in a world which yet enthralled her. She was troubled from a very
young age.

This feeling of alienation, despite bursts of calm, would remain
with her throughout her short life. Though she excelled in her
studies, Sophie left school at fifteen with no major qualifications,
hospitalised at the moment of her exams. She went to college in
Dundee, and after several prolonged and florid spells of psychosis,
battles with bulimia, alcoholism, and a diagnosis at 18 of severe
Bipolar Disorder, she gained the place at the University of St
Andrews she had set her heart on, age 20. But her demons returned,
and the story of her final twelve months is one of further psychotic
episodes, accompanied by a new diagnosis of Emotionally Unstable
Personality Disorder. Sophie details all of these experiences in her
writing with a unique blend of humour, lyricism, optimism and
humanity, which anyone who knew her will recognise.

On the evening of July 31st, 2016, Sophie decided to take her own
life, at the top of the Dundee Law – the extinct volcano which,
from below, provides the city's focal point, while granting from
its peak a panoptic view over the snaking wynds and closes of the
town, out past the Tay Bridge, and east to the North Sea.

SAMUEL REILLY (b. 1993), Sophie's brother, is a Glasgow-based
writer and researcher, who holds degrees from the University of
Oxford and the Courtauld Institute of Art. In 2016 he wrote and
edited the catalogue for *Masks, Music and Magic*, an exhibition of
African arts at The Hidden Lane Gallery, Glasgow. His poetry has
appeared in The Missing Slate and the Glasgow Review of Books,
and in 2012, he won the Oxonian Review Short Story Competition.

In loving memory of

Sophie Alexandra Reilly,

1995 - 2016

If I could do just one near-perfect thing,

I'd be happy.

Belle & Sebastian

TIGERISH WATERS

SELECTED WRITINGS OF
SOPHIE REILLY

Edited with an introduction by
SAMUEL REILLY

Published by Mad Weir Books Ltd, 2017

Printed in Scotland by Airdrie Print
24 - 26 Flowerhill Street
Airdrie, North Lanarkshire
Scotland
ML6 6BH

www.tigerishwaters.co.uk

Material quoted from Belle and Sebastian, from the song 'If She Wants Me', is printed here with the kind permission of the artists, © Belle and Sebastian, 2003.

Material quoted from Louis MacNeice, 'Entirely' (1940) is from *The Collected Poems of Louis MacNeice*, edited by E.R. Dodds (London: Faber & Faber, 1979). Used by permission of David Higham Associates, Ltd.

Cover Image: Tim Reilly, *Tigerish Waters.* © Tim Reilly, 2017

All profits from this book will be donated to **SAMH,** the **Scottish Association for Mental Health.**
Scottish Charity: No. SC-008897
Registered Office: Brunswick House, 51 Wilson Street, Glasgow, G1 1UZ

ISBN: 978-1-5272-1455-2

CONTENTS

Foreword   ix

Introduction by Samuel Reilly   xi

THE TAXI DRIVER   1

BEFORE THE SNUFF OF THE LIGHTS   11

POEMS   29
-     Untitled   31
-     13:30AM   32
-     Drives   36
-     Look Up   37
-     Birth and Growth   38
-     Prayer   40
-     Sunset Song   42
-     A Good Day   43

THE LAST MONTHS' JOURNAL   45

Foreword

In her piece on 'Mental Health Pride', from her 'Last Months' Journal', Sophie Reilly reflects that 'we are people, not diagnoses'. The sentiment is an important one. Like much else in this powerful book, it is also beautifully crafted.

We at SAMH, the Scottish Association for Mental Health, are delighted to lend our support to *Tigerish Waters* – the brave and honest account of Sophie's struggle with mental ill health. SAMH has represented the voice of people affected by mental health issues in Scotland for more than 90 years. Currently operating in 60 communities across Scotland, SAMH provides mental health social care support, homelessness, addictions and employment services, among others.

These services, together with national programme work in See Me, respect*me*, suicide prevention, sport and physical activity; inform SAMH's policy and campaign work to influence positive social change.

Knowing how important it can be to open up and talk, we hope that those who read *Tigerish Waters* will be encouraged to start their own conversation.

Jo Anderson
Director of External Affairs
SAMH

And if the world were black or white entirely,
And all the charts were plain,
Instead of a mad weir of tigerish waters,
A prism of delight and pain,
We might be surer where we wished to go,
Or again we might be merely
Bored but in brute reality there is no
Road that is right entirely.

- Louis MacNeice, 'Entirely'

Introduction

'Pandemic: The Fag Markets Crash' was one day to be the prologue of Sophie's memoir. Sometime towards the end of 2015, she called me to let me know she couldn't after all come and stay with me on a night-pass from hospital – a few of the inpatients had showed flu-like symptoms, which had been diagnosed variously (on the ground) as 'swine flu', 'bird flu', and 'pishing your shits'. A general quarantine had been enforced; she explained on the phone, with manic proliferation of detail, how the lockdown had cut off cigarette supplies at source and was jeopardising the intricate exchange-economy which had developed on the wards, with the fag as its central currency. Hyperinflation, utter panic, was ensuing. A schizophrenic, whom Sophie dubbed "The Chancellor", had been long in the habit of emotionally blackmailing tabs, dividing them into two or three roll-ups and selling them on at the OAP ward when cash (usually a rather less important commodity) was scarce – at that time he happened to have a fair reserve stashed up and the prices he began to command threatened to rend the usually quite harmonious wee community asunder. Those who could afford them with any kind of regularity, harassed with the pleading of others, were forced to demand favours well beyond what custom had decreed fair and workable – a coffee became a takeaway pizza; a dram became a bottle; friendships formed over weeks were now being called, maliciously, into question, and the nurses were becoming increasingly frantic in failing to reassert authority and order.

Sophie was revelling in the wild absurdity of her microcosm, embellishing at will, caricaturing the nurses by imbuing them with an evil, vindictive glee in their role as enforcers, painting the 'plague-victims' as beleaguered war heroes emerging shaken, but victorious, from their battles with the bog. She was probably putting a certain comic distance between this world and herself – but the mind has a strange proclivity to draw back, to characterise, at the moment it is most immersed, and even then, she was adamant about how central the experience must be to her life. A part of her was to consist of casting these individuals, the patients she had forged such close relationships with through their shared deprivations, in a drama which would humanise their suffering, their conditions, flesh out their stigmata, and help her realise what she herself had been through.

Such an ambition called for a few years' distance and stability to see it through, but Sophie only had a frenzied eight months left. In the final section of this volume, which covers this period, we find its only, elusive expression – she alludes to the 'stories these people in hospital can tell', which could have us in stitches but which couldn't yet be told, for that would be to break 'the unwritten but holy confidentiality between patients'. So, instead, we have a short journal – a piece of life-writing, created over several months, that marks the means by which Sophie alternately grasped and lost control of herself. There is a broader political urge for 'mental health pride', and, through it all, a constant sense of struggling against oppressors who, if they often manifest as external, are just as often acknowledged as products of her own mind.

Soph'd managed to argue her way out of her section

by early January and was discharged, high and wild, to run through the ESA benefits she'd accrued in hospital, flitting from hotel to hotel across the East of Scotland, almost willing herself to burn out. I tried to visit her in Dundee for her twenty-first birthday, arriving only to find she had moved on. A couple of weeks later, I was tracked down via email by the kind and deeply concerned proprietor of an Inn where she had spent a few blissful nights, before accidentally trashing the place (fag burns and spilt booze, I've imagined), plugging the sink and leaving it running, falling down the stairs and being carted off by the police to hospital. Soon after this, she was admitted to a homeless hostel in Dundew. Here she wrote 'The Joys of Destitution', trying again to distil vital experience from a period of hardship – I love this little piece, where from time to time she sprinkles over a chatty, very unpretentious, twenty-first-century idiom more poetic colloquialisms; 'God is handing out lollies'. It exhibits what she calls 'that tiny bit of tenacity mental illness didn't obliterate after all'. She fell passionately in love in the hostel, with a boy whom she made a desperate effort to save from association with a cruel local gang who named themselves the 'spunk merchants', and, to the despair of the staff, she scrawled defiantly on every wall in sight – little in-jokes and quotes from songs and scattered verses (she showed me pictures, when I saw her in April, which are lost, though one of the strange and desperate poems has been recovered, and is printed here as 'Done-For Dee').

Even though the most subtly moving, the most concerted pieces of writing were produced during the few years prior, it seems important to me to introduce Sophie as she was at this time. Perhaps, in part, it's because this is when she's hardest to pin down – vitriol and compassion, self-worship and self-loathing are pitted in violent conflict

– but I think I'm also drawn to remembering her like this because it's like this she embodies, tragically, the concerns which were always central to her. The battle with Bipolar, with Borderline Personality Disorder and with prolonged psychotic episodes was never in itself supposed to be her high water-mark. What she wanted, always, was to reach a point in life where her mind would relax its assault, open to the wide beauty of the human world around her, and let her at last position herself in its context. But the final section of this volume, for all the flashes of huge and generous hope, is an account of such a mind gradually losing control. She finally burnt out in June, and as far as I know she wrote no more in the final six weeks she passed quietly, filled with shame and regret for the wild excesses of her psychotic months, in a psychiatric hospital in Dundee. She absconded on July 31st – telling the nurse who granted her the day-pass that yes, she was feeling much happier, thanks – to Dundee Law, where she was found the next day. She left no note; she had said it all already.

For this extraordinary girl, the ordinary was always slipping further beyond reach. This is what seems to me essential about this volume, what gets us closest to the particular wit and imagination my sister always showed. Mental illness tends to have us thinking in hushed tones. Maybe this is because we see it as a threat to that sense of our own self-worth, which we find simply in our ability to maintain a rational, productive, day-to-day mentality. Or else – and I've been thinking more and more that this may just be the other side of that coin – it's because we idealise the darker reaches of the mind as the province of a liberated genius, which has dared to discover merely the audacity it takes to venture there. When we think of Sylvia Plath's last poems, for example, we see a premonition of her suicide which fuses with the black majesty of the work itself, calling upon the work to justify a perceived transgression against life. Sophie's is a different story – more likely, but less often told – of a talent defining itself in opposition to the mental anguish which caused the continual ebb of her ability to focus and thus, really, to live up to herself. Not world-weariness, but an inviolable faith in a world from which she felt herself cruelly excluded.

So, when we read the frantic, fragmented journal that emerges from the last few months, we should keep in mind the deeply human figure of the driver in 'The Taxi Driver' (2014), around whose fundamental kindness and empathy this lively story is structured. Succour and relief sparked my sister into the most aching, lyrical appreciations of her life; two poems from 2015 – 'Sunset Song' (named after the Grassic Gibbon novel she once termed 'The Scottish Bible') and 'Prayer' – stand here as beautiful witnesses to this. It is impossible to read these, along with the one-act play she produced at seventeen – 'Before the Snuff of the Lights' (2012) – and not regret there isn't more like it, that she never in her brief adult life experienced a period of enough stability to sustain her, in her wonder and her zeal, long enough to realise her talents, to craft what would have been a touching, lyrical memoir and preface it with the great fag market crash.

Since so little of what we print here in its stead was intended for publication (except sometimes on social media), I have had to ask a difficult question of myself as regards my responsibility as an editor: do I print everything faithfully, exactly as it was written, or should I listen to my feeling that sometimes the most essential moments, emerging from unstructured, unpremeditated passages, suffer from their surroundings? Someone close to me suggested that I consider Sophie looking back herself, in five years' time, at these pieces; if she was preparing the experience of life and of illness recorded in them for publication, how would she have wanted them to appear? I have taken this advice, trying to exercise as light a touch as possible when it comes to the works more obviously intended for an audience, but otherwise considering it duty to construct from the fragments – many more of which are profoundly personal attempts to work out her own meaning than forays into literary form – a narrative. One which both celebrates Sophie's huge facility for imagery and turn of phrase – which always inflicted upon me a burning sense of sibling-jealousy, ever since we were young – but also does justice to her life.

Sophie was driven to great and terrible self-knowledge, but retained a remarkable receptiveness to all that is compassionate in our world. With a vibrant originality, her voice, both in her despair and her soaring euphoria, calls upon all of us who have ever felt the kinds of tormenting illness she suffered to be beyond our comprehension or our concern, and offers itself to those who still struggle silently, wishing, with Sophie in 'Before the Snuff of the Lights', that their story could reach out to these strangers for whom life comes more easily, and 'brush their veneers with its fingertips'.

SAMUEL REILLY

THE TAXI DRIVER

(2014)

She was small as she stood in the rain. Her usual air of magic and charm had been dissipated in the Glasgow drizzle, her manic hair dangling limply over wide, rabbit's eyes. Tall as she was, her twig of a body was dwarfed by the sodden suitcases littering her feet, a bin bag on its last legs, a grumpy cat's cage perched atop a filthy bag of soil. A rush of cold engulfed her bridge as a train thundered underfoot, and she brought her nylon furs closer, bright leopard print against the storm-blue sky.

Pure baltic eh day, i'nt it?
Aye, I'm bloody freezin'.
Want me eh turn eh heatin' up, hen?
Naw, you're awright.
There's a boundary charge fer this, sweetheart, 'sat awright?
Aye.

The third taxi of the day swished its way around the corner and rumbled towards the funny creature. This coincided with 'A Change is Gonna Come' starting up in her ears. She saw some meaning in it and laughed.

Wantin' a hand wae aw that, hen?
Aye, please.

Raindrops were lit up like fireflies in the arcs of headlight beams. Rough hands and grunts carried her things to the boot, and she fell into the back seat, kicking off her heels.

Carsevale, please.

She felt the car rumble beneath her and melted into warmth and safety. Taxis had been her home for the last few months. She always sought solace in letting someone else take the responsibility for her survival for a while. Plus, she loved taxi drivers. Great banter, tell them anything, never see them again. The perfect friends.

'Ye visitin' someb'dy?'

'Naw, startin' work.'

'Aw right. Sorry, ye just looked aw dressed up.'

'Nah I'll change intae my shit when ah git in.'

'Fair dos. Ye look crackin' but.'

She beamed. She really loved taxi drivers – especially when she was in her heels and furs, her signature battle armour.

'Cheers.'

'Wit the fuck ye daein' wae a load ae compost?'

'Emm..'

'Sorry, 'sit awright if I swear, like?'

'Aye, course it fuckin' is.'

He chuckled, almost fondly.

'Ah wis daein' a load ae plantin' at ma boyfriend's hoose.'

'Aw right. Hope ye got changed.'

'Nah, it wis only inside stuff. Hoose plants an' aht.'

'Hoose plants an' a cat isnae the best shout.'

'Nah the cat lives wae me. Ah wis just gaein' him a shot eh her.'

'If she pees on ma carpet it's 50 quid.'

'Deal.'

'Or a kiss.'

'Get tae fuck.'

He snorted in appreciation. He was certainly fanciable. Youngish, smiley, rough around the edges. Looked a bit like her old History teacher. She began to imagine a love scene between them and giggled. He could be her new soulmate. Why the fuck not? Life is short. You only live once. Live for the moment. Just Do It.

'Carpe diem.'

'Wit?'

She'd let her mind spill into her mouth again. She needed to stop that. People were getting in.

'Nothin, jist talkin tae masel.'

'I dinnae allow Latin in ma taxi, hen.'

She giggled again. Definitely fanciable. She decided to make him fall in love with her.

'Although I agree wae the sentiment.'

'Good stuff, me too.'

'So how's yer day been? Seized enough?'

'Too right, haven'y stopped the day.'

'How come?'

Her eyes alighted as she readied her story.

'Well I hud tae git across the toon tae ma parent's hoose in Giffnock tae pick up the cat and stuff, then tae the garden centre in the Mearns, then tae ma boyfriend's flat in Cambuslang, then deal wae him an aw his shite, then git the train back intae toon wae all this crap and now intae work.'

'Christ, fair dos. D'ye really lug a cat the whole way just

tae gie him a shot? Wee hing mus'be knackered.'

'Aye, well she's good fer him.'

'Nice lassie you are.'

'I try.'

'Could he not jis come see her?'

'Naw, ma parents pure hate him. Plus he's no really well jis now.'

Two very personal revelations now lay in the air, and in the pause before he spoke she tingled, holding the frozen moment as long as she could. She loved anticipation, these Schrodinger's-cat seconds where the future hung divided, thrilling her with possibilities. A miaow broke the magic. Shut it Fluffles. Wish I'd called you Schrodie.

'Sorry to hear that, hen.'

She jolted back to earth. He sounded genuinely regretful. She hid her gleeful smile.

'Och, it's awright. He's just on his own s'much the now. Tryin tae brighten the place up wae plants an' paintings n aht, but ah dunno if he's even noticed, the muppet.'

'Ah'm sure he will've, gorgeous.'

'Oh so it's gorgeous, now, is it?'

'Well, yer bein' such a doll tae him. Luggin' a cat across a city. It's a gorgeous hing tae dae.'

She was taken aback. She had been counting on manageable, scripted sexual banter. Compliments of a more profound nature were a new territory. She decided to put one toe into it.

'Thanks. Ah really do try. Gets pretty hard, sometimes, when he's really ill.'

'Is it cheeky tae ask wit's wrang wae him?'

'Aye, very.'

'Shit.'

'I don't mind though. Depression.'

'Whit a fucker. Especially wae your job.'

'Ah know man, cannae git away from bonkers cunts.'

'Shouldnae say that hen!'

'Ah know, bit it's true. Madness is everywhere in ma life. Ma life is madness.'

Her flippant tone broke and betrayed a sliver of bitterness. She was angry now. Angry and talking.

'Dae everythin' fer that cunt. Wash his clothes, buy his food, buy his drink, cuddle him, pay his bills, clean his hoose, make his dinner, take him tae his appointments, wash his blood aff the carpet when he throws a radgy. Never says thank you. Never asks aboot me. Jist whinges aboot how miserable he is. Ma life is takin care of the sook.'

'Gottae mind he's no well, hen.'

'Believe me, ah mind it. Why'd ye hink ah dae it all in the first place? I want the fucker tae be happy. I want tae make him better.'

'No as simple as aw that.'

'No. Not simple. No fuckin' simple at aw. Like I can make anybidy better. Cannae even make masel better. Just make everyhin' worse.'

She bit her lip, hid a little gasp and blinked through tears at him in the rearview mirror. He looked concerned – that type of sombre reticence which had possessed her parents, her teachers, her nurses, her doctors, the whole lot of "grown-ups" who discussed her soberly when she was out of the room. She had bared herself too much. A brisk wipe of the tears, a busy shuffle of the coat – she gathered herself back in.

'Sweetheart, please dinnae be offended. But are ye really a nurse?'

'Naw, I'm a doctor.'

'Yer a bit young an pretty tae be a doctor, hen.'

'You sexist fuck.'

'Ye know whit ah mean.'

She sniffed despite herself and broke the edge of the silence.

'Ma sister wis in Carsevale, sweetheart. Broke wir hearts, so it did. She's fine now, goat three kids and a puppy, bit she wis in an oot fer years. Every time she wis in she'd cim oot wae a new boyfriend. Seemed tae think he was her soulmate, that they were two lost souls meetin in the madhoose, or somethin, and they'd get better if they hid each other tae face the world wae. Was quite poetic, actually. Ayewis ended badly, but. Never a gid shout tae start a relationship when yer oot o' yer box. Ye tend tae choose badly. Yer so vulnerable, tae.'

Orange slices of light from streetlamps came to a halt across her stunned face. Every ounce of her was coaxing back the tears from falling.

'That's seven pound, hen. Sorry if ah wis oot eh order.'

'Naw, it's ok.'

She scrambled for change, and watched his rough thumb kiss her palm as she handed him the coins. She felt warm at his touch. He jumped out of the cab and stomped round to release her appendages. Her hand stroked the cold steel of the door handle. She didn't want to go.

The scrambling stopped, and she was standing once more amongst her dripping belongings in front of a painfully white sign.

'Look after yersel, sweetheart. Ah mean that, right. Jist you get better. The rest o' it can get tae fuck.'

As she watched his kind face form the strange shapes of comfort, a tear betrayed her. She shrank under her voluminous furs and, as the car purred away, she tottered up towards the patient entrance, wondering what the hell they were going to say about the cat.

BEFORE THE SNUFF
OF THE LIGHTS

(2012)

LIVVY   I wish I could write a book. About my life, a really good one with critical merit and metaphorical prowess that would really touch people - make an imprint on their lives, make them think about me. Make everything I've lived through mean something to others besides my family, people I don't know, strangers in the street that will carry on with their lives but with my story having brushed their veneers with my fingertips. That's so much more beautiful, somehow – feeling something real for someone you don't even know. I suppose that's the seduction of fame, even at the most basic, disgusting, plastic surgery and whirlwind marriage level, although none of those 'celebrities' know it – some sort of innate desire we all have to leave something indelible behind, to confirm our existence by making it have an impact. And if it's on a stranger, then it's more real, I suppose. Our families have to love us, have to care, or there are consequences – guilt, judgement. A stranger is free to cast us aside, they have the free choice of paying us any attention at all, and if they choose to care, we must be worth caring about. I want to know for sure I'm worth caring about.

LUKE   So why don't you write it? You've enough
              material.

LIVVY   I want to. I've started so many times – my
              life is littered with the introductions of
              promising failures.

LUKE   Fuck up.

LIVVY   Fine, fine – but I can never get past the first
              few pages. I sort of realise that there's no
              point continuing, because the end will never
              come. Like, it will never be good enough
              – perfect enough. It'll never be all the
              romanticised beautiful crescendoing banging
              orgastic stunning PERFECTION I want it
              to be. It'll never be the stunning finale before
              the snuff of the lights.

LUKE   But the lights haven't blacked out, yet. You're
              still very much shining.

LIVVY   Yuck.

LUKE   Sorry, sorry – illuminated, then. Living.
              You're still alive, so the symphony hasn't
              ended yet, right? Why does it have to end
              with a finale?

LIVVY   Because it has to be beyond me. It has to

be better – it's my chance to make my life beautiful, take the best bits, craft it masterfully to extract its full impact. It has to end with a spill of emotion that's beyond reality. It has to be... I don't know, it has to be...

LUKE   Inhuman?

LIVVY   Yeah!

LUKE   Then that's not an autobiography.

LIVVY   Well, no, I suppose not.

LUKE   It's a fantasy. It's what you want your life to be, what your wildest dreams of glory are. You're living in cloud cuckoo land, Liv.

LIVVY   It's much better than reality. Life, in my experience, is just a series of distractions from how shit reality is.

LUKE   Bullshit.

LIVVY   No, it's true, and it's true for everyone. Why do you think alcohol is the national drug? Booze is part of our social fabric, everything's based around it. And why? Because it dulls your nerve endings. Physical and emotional. All the firing receptors that are feeding your brain with a constant barrage of misery and doubt and fear and disappointment are clouded, you're offered physical respite. Emotionally, everything is heightened. When you're drunk you laugh longer, cry harder, everything is more than it really is. Everything seems more alive. And psychologically, well, there's nothing better than being offered a simple numerical focus. Drink as much as you possibly can, as cheaply as possible, as quickly as possible. Oh fuck, I lost my job... DRINK! Oh fuck, I put on weight, DRINK! Oh fuck, I'm tired, DRINK! Oh fuck, the hole in my chest is opening up again, I need to fill it with DRINK! DRINK! DRINK!

LUKE   Are you trying to tell me you're an alcoholic?

LIVVY   No! I'm too poor for that shit.

LUKE   You smoke 20 a day.

LIVVY   That's different. That's mindful self-destruction. No pharmaceutical dulling, there, you remember every puff, feel it drawlingly poison your lungs. Fucking gorgeous.

LUKE   Why the hell are you trying to self-destruct?

LIVVY   What kind of a stupid question is that?

           (pause)

           I thought you knew this?

LUKE   I did, I suppose. But I had to ask.

LIVVY   Why?

LUKE   Because if I didn't then I'd hate myself.

LIVVY   Join the club.

LUKE   Jesus, Livvy, will you stop it?

LIVVY   What?!

LUKE   Stop nonchalantly throwing around bullshit,
           terrifying stuff like that, it's not exactly
           pleasant for the rest of us. Look, I know you,
           I know it's how you deal with it, this kind
           of wry, dark humour, but Jesus it makes me
           sick to my stomach. You don't have to be
           so fucking cynical about it, nobody in the
           world knows themselves that well. Probably
           because they don't spend nearly as much
           time as you do sitting around on their arses
           analysing the fuck out of every facet of their
           personality.

LIVVY   So I'm self-obsessed?

LUKE   I thought you knew this about you.

LIVVY   Fuck you!

LUKE   Oh, so you can abuse yourself, fine, but as
           soon as some mild criticism comes from the
           external universe you're all spitting defence?
           Stop it.

LIVVY   Stop what, exactly?

LUKE   Being so fucking contrary.

LIVVY   Fine. I'll shut up. I'm just talking, just spilling,
           just venting all the shit that stirs round in my
           mind every minute of every fucking day, but
           if it makes you uncomfortable...

LUKE   You can stop that, as well. Using the fact that
           you're fucked up as an excuse.

LIVVY   Don't you think I'm entitled?

LUKE   No, I don't. For the majority of the stigma-
           riddled, pussy population then knock
           yourself out, make your life easier by citing
           your diagnoses like get-out-of-jail-free cards,
           but don't try that on me. It's insulting. I know

you too well.

LIVVY   You barely know me at all!

LUKE   No, you barely know me at all. Because
               my entire function in this relationship is to
               reflect you back to you. You stand there for
               hours on end ranting convoluted crap that
               spurts out of your mouth as you enter the
               millionth dimension of over-analysis, and I
               listen. And sometimes, when you pause for
               breath, I hazard a small deflection. Hoping
               that you'll see everything you just said was
               bullshit. But no, you find every minute fault
               with my argument and carry on with your
               spiel even more violently than before.

LIVVY   Then why don't you just fuck off!

LUKE   Because, despite my best efforts, every new
               bullshit rant enraptures me more than the
               last.

LIVVY   I suppose that's your payment.

LUKE   Payment?

LIVVY   For my complimentary psychoanalysis.
               Except, as it turns out, it's anything but
               complimentary.

LUKE   What do you mean?

LIVVY   I mean a compliment might be quite fucking nice right now!

LUKE   Congratulations.

LIVVY   For what?

LUKE   'A compliment might be quite fucking nice right now'. You have hereby diagnosed and suggested a cure for your entire psychological chasm. You need to fill it with approval.

LIVVY   That's so Freudian I could puke.

LUKE   How so?

LIVVY   Oh, baby, fill my chasm with your juicy approval.

LUKE   Well, it's true.

LIVVY   I know it's fucking true! I'm well aware of my approval complex! Have been for years, thanks.

LUKE   Then why haven't you changed?

LIVVY   Because I don't know how!

LUKE   Once more, bullshit. You just don't want to
            change.

LIVVY   So you're saying I'm deliberately unhappy?

LUKE   Well, no, not deliberately, that's too direct.
            But on some level of your crazy mind
            there's something stopping you from healing.
            Becoming normal. You love being fucked up
            too much.

LIVVY   Excuse me?!

LUKE   I'm not saying you're faking, or attention-
            seeking or pretending or anything. I'm not
            saying 'buck up', I know how hard you try
            to drag yourself out of this hole. But admit
            it, you wear this thing on your chest like a
            medal. It's your excuse for being who you
            are – you're not Livvy, you're an illness,
            and therefore not responsible for yourself.
            You shove it in people's faces so they know
            that you're fucked up because you're ill, not
            because you yourself are damaged. And if
            you actually got better your mask would fall
            away.

LIVVY   I'm sorry.

LUKE   See? It just fell away. Underneath all that

visceral bite is you, and you're wounded.

LIVVY   I know.

LUKE   People have much more sympathy for wounds they can see than wounds they're told about.

LIVVY   I don't want to be pitied!

LUKE   I know. But you need to be. Just for a while.

LIVVY   So I should go back home? Lie in my mother's arms unwashed and crying for months on end again, is that it, I just need rest and recuperation and I'll be right as rain?

LUKE   No. I don't know what you need. I have no psychology degree and to be honest I doubt even almost anyone who does would have a fucking clue what to do with you.

LIVVY   Sorry to exasperate you.

LUKE   Don't be. I mean I am exasperated beyond belief, but don't be sorry.

LIVVY   No, I really am. I just use you as a verbal punching-bag.

LUKE   I don't mind.

LIVVY   No, we sit in this fucking room for hours on
            end, day after day, cigarette after cigarette
            and the whole place is more full of my hot
            air than smoke.

LUKE   Don't send it back in. Plus, it's useful in some
            ways. For your romanticised dreams. I'm
            still a stranger, and I've spent all this time
            listening.

LIVVY   Yeah, but not voluntarily. I've hypnotised you
            with my siren spout of wanky pseudopoetry.

LUKE   Oh, so you're in control here?

LIVVY   Damn right.

LUKE   Au revoir, Cherie... *(makes to leave)*

LIVVY   No, no, no !

            (She grabs his hand and pulls him back)

LUKE   My point exactly.

            (pause)

            I couldn't have left.

LIVVY   I know.

LUKE   Bullshit, you shat your pants.

LIVVY   I did not!

LUKE   *(imitating)* I did not! What, why's your lip trembling, like a little girl's?

LIVVY   You make me feel like a little girl.

LUKE   Now that, is disgustingly Freudian.

LIVVY   *(whips round)* You can't strip me down to nothing, to my bare pink quick and then take the piss out of what's left cowering! I feel sick.

LUKE   I don't understand...

LIVVY   Well you should! Like you said, I have a protective mask, and when you've ripped it off and made me vulnerable again you can't just flip right back to where we were before! Multiple personalities!

LUKE   You do not have multiple personalities, you can forget about that pill.

LIVVY   No, I don't mean that, I just... I feel weird. I

feel sick. I don't feel like me.

LUKE Do you ever feel like you?

LIVVY I feel like something, and that something's familiar. It's a fucking horrible narcissistic cynical bitch of a something, but I know it.

LUKE And now you feel like the ground's dropped out from under your feet.

LIVVY I... yeah. How..?

LUKE I'm sorry.

LIVVY Please catch me.

LUKE You're not falling. You're right here.

LIVVY I feel like I never stop falling.

LUKE I think we all do, sometimes.

LIVVY I wouldn't know.

LUKE We all get that thing of waking up from a dream convinced we're in mid-air about to plummet to oblivion.

LIVVY That's exactly it. The ice in my chest.

LUKE   But it slowly melts, doesn't it? As we realise
            we're safe, it melts and turns placid. Warm.
            Maybe this is part of waking up.

LIVVY   I'm so cold.

LUKE   Here. *(He wraps his arms around her).* Jesus, I
            think I preferred the aggressive nutcase.
            What have I done?

            (Livvy laughs, muffled by his shoulder)

LIVVY   You're not a stranger, Luke.

LUKE   Nope, I'm stranger than that.

LIVVY   Not at all. I can feel you.

LUKE   What?! Well it is fucking cold in here...

LIVVY   No you dipshit, I mean you reach me. The
            inner layer, you know, the real thing.

LUKE   Oh shit, what have I got myself into?

LIVVY   I know. Get the hell out, these are dangerous
            waters.

LUKE   Sharks swim through your veins.

LIVVY   I'm broken.

LUKE   You're a broken bloody record, but you're
             not broken. Just stop fucking thinking.

LIVVY   What, like it's so easy?!

LUKE   Imagine you're on a warm, sandy beach...

LIVVY   *(laughing)* Fuck up.

POEMS

UNTITLED

I remember, sometimes,
In transporting flashes
That light the paths
To our past,
A song you loved and derided
Within the same year.
Your tastes changed with your ripening mind,
So quick, and so darting –
I tried for so long to keep pace.

The solidity of mutual childhood
The vicious pinches and slobbery kisses
Proved itself ductile and stretched
Almost to invisibility –
A gossamer thread from my heart to your heels,
Out of sight in the distance,
In the promised land of your life.

I trudged on, snotty, in your wake.

But on this road of my pilgrimage,
As I happened upon your discarded relics,
I found them bitter, and reluctant
To reveal their secrets again.

(c. 2011)

13:30 AM

I awake, dirty, and my head implodes.
Clambering out through my somnolent opiate
Into the fetid world to face another day –
Five minutes, maybe, a day jeers from the black.
Stretch, shrivel, cosy up
Under the bedsheets stinking of my sleeping
    presence
But the sleep has gone, the oblivion snatched
And I tumble to the floor.
I'm half asleep, still almost dreaming
Of shadows of moods and just-elapsed terrors
So cling to it, sweep with the wave of languor
Stumbling down to the bathroom.

Pee first, scales next.
And now my deadened heart begins
To stir, promised its one daily risk.
This kind of terror slays a soul,
Lays waste to brains, blackens inside
Yet still, among the carnage, leaves
A tenacious, triumphant, puling wish
To be less.
A scrape of tile over candour
Strokes my spine with intimate dread –
This is the modern woman's flagellation,
The daily ritual of the almost-dead.

The scales say I'm thin.
I say, I don't care.
And something in me smirks and shrieks
At the vile injustice of teenage dreams
To lose 'a stone' – a unit, an end
Which on completion swears to pay
The bearer on demand a prize
Of tantalizing mystery –
I'll be happy, I said,
And believed it, too.

So I'm staring out a black machine
Whose mythical symbols have shrivelled and died
Like yesterday's blooms on Eden's compost pile.
The walls don't dissolve to reveal a new world –
They stare down, defiant, relentlessly silent,
Their gaze smothering a skinnier me.

Stagger, only just numb still, in search
Of my next ration of stirring.
Foul spitting fluid poured down the throat
To erode the unseen within.
My hand slips, and some spills,
And spreads in a placid pool,
Loitering for just a brisk striding wipe –
But it's enough, a jutting jar
To jolt the wires from their drowse
In my cavernous chest – they stir, and resume
Their sickly vibration.

Oh Hell: An ecstasy
Of locks and lovely solid keys
Before the fresh and searing air.
The promise of one song's tinny duration,
Legitimate, abetting, noxious occupation.
Crumble to heap of greasy bones and sour cotton
On a clatty back step swathed in my past eons'
    ash.

My furtive grunge is contagious.
Fag ends dribbling out the stone's buried cracks
Like my own putrid slime trail.
But my instincts betray my faithful subordination
In glancing briefly at the sky.

The cerulean radiance
Kisses the world,
Sunbeams gently coax
The vital from the cell
But I can't see it.
I can't feel it.
I am stone, millennia cold.

And the wires pulsate
With their menacing glee
Wickedly aroused
There's a screech in my ears
And hooks in my eyes
And a roar in my chest
That's going to burst –

The wires snap, swift slack
Sky falls, before my eyes.
It falls out of the bottom of the world.

Mewling in the shards,
A pining whimper:
Plea of the heart
I am.

Breathe.
Flick the flint with my sucked-raw thumb,
Gush sweet smoke.
Gauzily sift my
Mass into dust.

Pantomime exits;
Intrigue, and delight –
Smoke soaks the space
Whence my fairy took flight.

(2011)

DRIVES

I like the crashes.
They replace the wires
Vibrating in my chest
Until I twist and scream.
Pain is of no object;
It is the headline and the kill.
I am covered in blades.
My insides are made of glass.
Frissons from the metal
Through the layers of my mass
Lyrics written in my blood
That I don't quite understand.
I wish I was a poet
But I have no words to give –
Only sharpness, and blades, and the drive
    to be art.
I want my hair to paint my heart.

(2011)

LOOK UP

The sky groans with stars.
Webs of eccentricities
Yawning back through space and history.

Seductive velvet, punctured by life.

More and more, thick and fast;
My retinas sear with too much to bear
Of the truth, the concrete, the real.

I see my life mapped in erratic dots,
Memories burst from their sleep –
Sandy ice cream, playground fancies,
Burning nostrils and something strange
In the chest permeating everything –
A sort of unspecified longing,
A wistfulness, a reaching out
For something to cling to,
To melt my heart sculpted in ice.

Too much, too fast, remembrance stabs
My gut with realization –
I'm still a child, with sticky hands,
Screaming for salvation.

(2012)

BIRTH & GROWTH

The breath is caught
As we are entranced
In the pace of ever-changing skies,
Swirling beyond us to a horizon unknown,
Of futuristic whispers, laughing to scorn
Or to soothe; never certain are we,
Eternal ambiguity as far as we see.

The birth of the universe
Came to place in red;
Fires blazing with the heat of gods;
The quake of the earth as it came to be,
The screech preceding the existence of seas,
The oceans swelled and the hearts soared
With meteoric hurt, universal uproar:
A prologue of events the world should observe.

But while the universe ceased to scream,
The newborn humans were left to dream
Of a seemingly meaningless existence,
Raw with hurt, tender, supple,
Naïve skin, pink from the world's inclemency;
Like a foal's debut on its spindly legs
We expose ourselves to the world that begs
Of us our souls, demanding knowledge
In its insatiable thirst for perfection.

We have grown since then.
We are a new race, a new being,
But forever an asymptote to expectations,
Never enough to fit the gaping hole
Ripped from man at the inception of soul.
The hole that defines us, that makes us human,
The rip in our unfathomable condition.

Personality is a veil to conceal the hole,
To give us meaning.
The self is embroidered fabric.
We never know who we are.
Forever we remain,
A half-discovered soul,
A half-discovered self,
Reclining in our eternal gaze
At half-discovered stars
In a world of broken beauty.

(c.2014)

PRAYER

I prayed to God today.

It's not a common thing
It sprang up on me, this rush to speak
Like the bubbly urge of song.

I was at an altar,
Down below a stunning cathedral
Full of kindly whispers.

And so I couldn't hear
All the stabbing shouts of "Oh God"
Stemming from the panic
That fell away like silk
And left a love for life itself and
An innocent, pained wish.

It smelt of fresh, you see
And so I leapt and said "Hello, Lord
I don't believe in you,
But I know you'll listen.
I love you, really, for all you do
To give us passion, hope.

At six, I wrote to you.
Asked you to look after Mor-Mor
Launched it out the window

I saw it on the clouds.
Years later, I found it
In my mum's chestnut bedside table,
Imprinted still with soil.

People believe in life
They hug together, want to do good
Give me gentle faces
Pray for their blood, and so
I thank you for their spirit. I wish
I could believe. I do."

I stopped, tears welling up in
Eyes sparkling from the candles on
The table full of faith.
I thought, that maybe faith
Was not belief in gospel stories
But friends that make you whole and build
A hopeful-looking lens.

(May/June, 2015)

SUNSET SONG

The glistening pulse of the water's gleam
Draws my eyes into squinting hypnosis,
And the whip of the wind and the seagull's scream
Draws my love towards those I hold closest.

"Nothing endures but the land", she said,
Staring through sharp, gust-swept heath
And I echo the words in the peace that I get
From the water churning beneath.

Land birthing water, expanses drifting
Away to the swooping horizon –
As I stare out to sea I can feel something lifting;
Breathe, and enjoy this asylum.

(May/June, 2015)

A GOOD DAY

Little things
Nuances of light and sweet air
Toothsome as iced dew-soaked tea.
I gulp lungfuls, with the luscious fervour
Of a silver-slip fish in a crystalline pool,
And feel so intensely
The syrup of my soul's cleansing.

Small things
Awakening to a dawn drenched in time
And feeling soft arms envelop my heart,
The painful embrace, the pouring return
Of myself.

(undated)

THE LAST MONTHS' JOURNAL

MENTAL HEALTH PRIDE

Honestly, I think the LGBT Pride movement has caused some of the most amazing historical events I've seen with my own eyes in the last 20 years – Gays can get married, for pete's sake, it's like an emancipation proclamation!

I think now a new movement needs to happen, Mental Health Pride. We're here, we're crazy, get over it. Some people have mental illness, it's a fact of life, not a terrifying visualisation of strait jackets and gibbering lunatic asylums. We're all just normal people with families, (usually tragic) life stories, loves, cares, desires, eccentricities, who happen to have a problem with their brain. Whether that's psychological trauma or physical trauma, such as the chemical imbalance of depleted serotonin in Major Depressive Disorder, or the overactivity of the prefrontal cortex in Schizophrenia.

But we don't post photos of our suffering, terror, paranoia, misery, suicidality, mania, psychosis. We don't get the 100 comments of 'get well soon' or the flowers from everyone or the 'you're so brave fighting your illness!'

We are locked in loony bins and generally ignored until we get out and are generally expected to get on with it and get back to work.

We go through hell in here. We see terrifying visions of things that aren't there -

hallucinations of an attacker beating you, when in reality it's you punching yourself in the face; Frank from Donnie Darko is sitting at the end of your bed when you wake up. We feel so low and lonely and despise our own flesh so much that we starve it, or cut it, or burn it, or make it vomit, or kill it with booze and drugs, or even kill it on purpose. We go manic and lose all sense of reality and run around the country off our fucking trolleys and nearly getting killed, then crashing and being consumed with guilt for breaking up with your boyfriend because you believed you were the daughter of God and he was beneath you. Amongst a novel's-worth of excoriating, humiliating, mortifying escapades. And you crash further into depression until the guilt and lamentation leads you to attempt suicide.

But you survive. We are all survivors. We deal with our demons by swallowing different pills, going to different therapies, spending half of our bloody lives in Community Mental Health Team appointments and groups. And we get on with it.

Bent-double, like old beggars under sacks, knock-kneed, coughing like hags (from our 20-a-day habit), we curse through sludge.

We deserve anything but being thought of as merely 'crazy' or 'mental' or 'loopy' or 'schizo' or 'a screw loose' and never trusted, or taken seriously, as everyone's too fucking scared of us or thinks we're just broken or plain doesn't give a shit.

I'm hereby coming out as a mental case. I'm Sophie, I suffer from Anorexia Nervosa, Bulimia Nervosa, Bipolar Affective Disorder, Emotionally Unstable Personality Disorder - Impulsive Subtype, and Post-Traumatic Stress

Disorder.

But I'm also a qualified ESOL teacher, a volunteer at Oxfam and at L— in the elderly wards. I had to defer because I was very ill, but I'm going to St Andrews Uni next year to study Theology and Literature. And then maybe a psychology module just cause it'll be a piece of piss. I'm an expert through experience!

I love Sam Cooke and The Beatles all the way through to Bruno Mars and Arctic Monkeys. I like to map decades with the lyrics of their songs. I paint pastels when I can be assed and can play The Sims 3 for a week straight. I smoke Camels when I can afford them and Amber Leaf when I can't. I fancy the pants off Alex Vause in Orange is the New Black but she's a fucking Scientologist in real life and I'm heartbroken.

And without breaking the unwritten but holy confidentiality between patients, the stories these people in hospital can tell can give you a stitch from laughter.

This is not me showing off or going on about how brilliant I am. I can be a ROYAL PAIN IN THE ASS. But I'm a person, just like you.

We are people, not diagnoses.

~ **December 7, 2015** ~

So the most exciting thing to happen to me recently is an outbreak of illness in the ward. Rumours have called it 'swine flu,' 'bird flu,' 'diarrhoea and vomiting', 'pure coughing and chucking your guts up' and my favourite 'pishing your shits.' Infection control procedures came in so we were basically quarantined. No one in, no one out. Nurses were all wearing masks, gloves and aprons. Healthy patients disappeared one by one, and we all speculated over who would be the next to succumb to the plague. The corridor reverberating with coughing and retching like it was haunted by a hungover ghost. The garden covered by puke; the pigeons eating the puke; the pigeons squawking their last probably somewhere up behind Lidl.

But the best bit was the global cigarette crisis. At least 80% of the patients here smoke, and cigarettes are the currency (with a small black market in hash). A pack of fags is worth its weight in gold to someone with no time out - and now no one had time out. The kind ones shared; the canny ones got them posted through windows, one somehow procured a box of duty free and was doing 50p a fag. One complete GENIUS of an elderly man developed a scam of picking doubts off the floor to pique people's sympathy so they would offer him a cigarette... And then making 3 roll ups out of them and selling them on. Money? Everyone had money. But our smokes were running out, and the fear was getting real. Our own little microcosmic sample of the failing economy, represented by the pricelessness of a fag when you've not had one for 5 hours and you've got nothing to do but watch Jeremy Kyle and listen to a playlist of puking – it was quite a fitting soundtrack, actually.

And then suddenly the restrictions were lifted, the fallen soldiers returned and regaled us with their battles with the toilet, and life was back to normal, the gossip returning to who was stealing whose Irn Bru.

I keep saying I'm gonna write a book about all this someday, and I've found my prologue.

'Pandemic: The Fag Markets Crash.'

~ December 11, 2015 ~

Dundee is a terrifying place.

It is steeped in history, and utterly beautiful in every way. Sunsets and sunrises are breathtaking in Dundee. The partial eclipse over the Tay was the most incredible experience of my life.

But this beautiful city is dying.

There is a beggar every one hundred feet.

Everything shuts at 11pm. Night time is a ghost town. And there are a lot of ghosts.

The ghosts of Desperate Dan, and the Bash Street Kids.

The ghosts of humming jute mills, churning out sandbags for the brave boys on the Western Front.

The ghosts of typewriters clanging in the Courier, changing the world one letter at a time.

The ghosts of Mother Jam, Father Ale, Uncle Black Pudding, Cousin Haggis, Aunty Bagpipes, Brother Kilt, Sister Ceilidh, Baby Irn Bru, and scary Uncle Buckfast who no one likes to talk about.

I had to go to college the morning after the referendum. Silence.

The buses weren't running.

An entire, beautiful city was grieving.

There is one psychiatric unit for the whole city. It is about the size of a small primary school, and has around 30 beds.

It breaks my heart living in Scotland.

~ January 6ᵗʰ ~

Florid mania and psychosis is the most terrifying thing in the world. I thought I was the Antichrist and possessed by the spirit of Anne Frank; the nurses were SS officers and they were trying to send me to the gas chambers. Took 8 of them to restrain me. I was hearing voices chanting in German and screeches of people being burnt. I could smell burning, and feel slimy hands touching me like seaweed.

And Skippy was back. He's a 10 foot kangaroo with the face of Frank from Donnie Darko who pops up everywhere when I least expect it. He's always in my nightmares but once psychosis blurs the line between dreams and reality he stalks me constantly.

Utterly fucking terrifying.

But I'm sane now!!! Well... These things are all relative!!

I'm so sorry for any bonkers messages and to anyone who suffered my bizarre behaviour. And so grateful to everyone who supported me whilst I lived out my own private horror film.

And I lived to tell the tale.

I feel so fucking strong right now. I survived hell on

earth. And I'm stoating about the open ward in leather thigh boots and a Harry Potter t-shirt singing Frank Turner at the top of my voice.

Oh yeah, a month without Internet and only allowed outside for 10 minutes ever two hours = hell. However, I have rediscovered the joys of the analogue world. I have learned to paint and draw, and I've learned the guitar! I've always said 80% of my brain is taken up by song lyrics...

And now I can sing them.

I've discovered how to get it out, the pain inside. I don't need to cut, or burn, or starve, or puke, or scream.

I just need to sing.

My emergency detention certificate runs out on Saturday, and I have my pre-discharge meeting in the morning to organise community care. Still homeless but planning on just staying in a youth hostel until I sort a private let. Will take months to go through the council, and I'm ready to get on with my life.

The next chapter awaits.

Oh... And I'm allowed out to the shops! Fags, juice, haribo.

That's all I'll ever need.

Soph xxxx

~ January 10th ~

I am still pretty fucking hypomanic right now...

But I've realised it, have cut off my bank card and am using a prepaid, have got myself a Nokia brick to use so I don't have Amazon and tinder and Facebook and the whole dangerous world of the Internet at my fingertips, I'm sitting in my hotel room watching QI pure gouched on quetiapine, and I've made an appointment with the Crisis Team in the morning.

I'm getting the hang of this shit.

~ January 11th ~

You, yourself, as much as anybody in the entire universe, deserve your love and affection. - Buddha

It's taboo nowadays to say 'I'm pretty' or 'I'm clever' or 'I'm a good listener' or 'I'm fit.' If you say anything positive about yourself, you're struck off as 'up yourself.'

Well, take it from me. You're not. You're just confident in your own abilities - which you damn well should be.

We live in a zeitgeist of self-disgust. And it's only us that can break the super-tight, suffocating mould.

Today, try looking at yourself in the mirror - and instead of immediately zoning in on your spots or blackheads or scars or wobbly bits or wonky teeth,

Try and look for something you like. Anything at all. A mole, the curve of your hip, just something that you can hold on to.

Then I dare you to look at yourself straight in the eyes and say 'I am a good looking person.'

It's a lot fucking harder than you think.

I still can't get the words out. It hurts too much to go against the self-hatred we are drip fed by the media and each other.

But I'll get there.

Be kind to yourself. Nobody is harsher on you than you.

~ January 15ᵗʰ ~

So I bit the bullet. I sold my iPhone.

I think it's the best decision I've ever made. And probably the scariest. Ranks way above declaring myself homeless. Felt utterly cut off from the world, spinning down into blackness...

But then... It wasn't blackness. It was Union Street. And I had nothing desperately precious in my hand with constant flicking, beeping, updating, snapping, PAY ATTENTION TO ME BING BING BING NOW NOW NOW!!!

I'm typing this from the iCafe on Sauchiehall Street. Once I've chatted and clicked about a bit I can finish my coffee, and go back outside, with no earphones.

So I can hear the buskers, and the bustle, and the snapshots of conversation, and the drunken ramblings, and the rumble of the Subway underfoot. And when I'm waiting for a bus... I can strike up a conversation.

And what I've learned is... people are MORE THAN HAPPY to chat. In Glasgow, anyway... but I think in this age of everybody UTTERLY ADDICTED to the

Internet, and the Internet and all its wonders and horrors at our fingertips, and we're unable to tear ourselves away... I think it's easy to forget that black and white text is not a conversation.

There's no eye contact. No body language. No joy at seeing someone's eyes light up when you make them laugh. No touching.

I think we're all lonely.

Also, I lost my purse and all my cards when I was bonkers(-er) and the letter with my new PIN has been lost in the nethersphere between L— and G—, so I've been living off £5 emergency cash a day. So I've inadvertently done a George Orwell. It's been eye opening to say the least.

I didn't have enough to buy a phone on Wednesday when I sold it, and all of yesterday I was in my hostel toilet with Norovirus. Had my ps3, a battered copy of Chamber of Secrets, and a Divine Comedy album to see me through.

I didn't find out Alan Rickman had died until this morning on the news.

Fucking freaky. In his last hours, he helped me through my pain, just like Harry Potter has helped me through since I was six years old, lying on my bedroom carpet listening to Stephen Fry cassette tapes with Fluffles my rabbit lolloping round my head, where I escaped into a world where I wasn't lost, but home.

Rest in Peace you wonderful man.

"After all this time?

...

Always."

S xxx

(p.s. – I now have a wee £20 phone from the 24 hour shop, and no contacts, so message me if you'd like my number...

That's the most presumptuous sentence I have ever typed.)

~ **February 6th** ~

Not ashamed.
    If all else fails,
    Tooth and claw.
    If the only way to get through hell is to be a Tiger,
    I say we're fucking endangered and they're killing us for the wonderful places we roam,
    and locking us in circus cages instead,
    But we will chew through the wires, swim up the Nile and bite you on the ass when you're not looking
    just cause you looked at us the wrong way.
    We Are Tigers.
    He's a fucking Lion.
    Save the Big Cats.
    Play this. It's free. Anybody who makes it into night 3,
    You can be a Calico or a Tortie. All Calicos/Torties are female.
    Only the Lions get through to the morning.
    And only the males get the fucking mane,
Except Lionee.

My big cousin gave her to me Christmas 1999.

It's stamped in Gold on her foot.

She did have bells but Sam cut them off with scissors
cause we were in bunk beds and he was a prick.

But Lionee has been in any bedroom i've ever had since I
was that 4 year old in the bottom bunk at the Millennium
and Y2K and I had my Christmas Lion.

With a big cosy mane.

And she was a she.

because why the hell shouldn't female lions have manes.

    We do all of the real fucking work anyway.

    i've got my stripes to prove it.

~ February 20th ~

Nobody who attempts or commits suicide wants to die.

    They just can't take the fucking pain of living any more,
so they reach for the ultimate painkiller, like a comfort
blanket of oblivion.

    Heaven, hell (for the masochists), reincarnation, paradise,
the great unknown, or just black... the whole roulette wheel
seems a washing relief from the pain inside. Whether that's
mental illness, or a break up, or loss or whatever it is that's
screwing the vice.

    If someone – that magic someone we are all searching
for but which so few of us find – would come along out
of the blue with a screwdriver and a snog... believe me,
we'd rather go out drinking and get laid and fall in love

and get our hearts broken and have our friends and family cook us noodle soup and hold our hands while we cry, and find out more about this fucking awesome world and the amazing people in it, which thrilled us once before we fell from grace, flat on our faces and bleeding.

We're not 'taking the easy way out', or committing some unforgivable sin, or weak,

we're just very tired, very sore, heartbroken, our heels are killing us, and we want to go home from the party and go to sleep.

We don't really want to leave. We still have a lot of dancing to do.

~March 10th ~

So yeah, life has been utterly fucking horrible for a very very long time. Pretty much every kinda crisis you could go through, it's been thrown at my face. Alcoholism, suicide, hospital/concentration camp, psychosis, mania, depression, pneumonia, norovirus, valium withdrawals, anorexia, bulimia, PTSD flashbacks, on the streets, in this dirtbox of a hostel surrounded by HIV positive thieves and minks and bastards and cunts...

And then one night I decide 'fuck it, 21 isn't THAT old, I'm fucking going out on the pull,' like I used to when I was young and free and the world hadn't gone to shit.

And I go to the union, basking in nostalgia of just how shitty it is and the dickhead rich bitches with vomit down their ballgowns and cuntish bouncers with a God complex...

And I give the manager a right royal telling off for all those times they threw me out to the street alone when I wasn't just drunk, I was skeletal and on huge amounts of meds inc. lorazepam...

(I'm still manic as fuck at this point, monologues go with the territory)

And ask someone for a fag. Fourth time lucky, it's not his 'last one' (everyone is perpetually on their last fag when it comes to people asking for one. Interesting...)

And then it turns out he's wearing a Smiths tshirt and is funny and clever and dorky and hot and is from Fahkin Essex Mate and we head off the St Andrews at 2am for no reason apart from it's pretty there.

And then a few weeks go by as I have had no phone or internet and living in this hostel is a full time fucking job, keeping yourself and your belongings safe.

And then I'm stealing internet in the Old Mill common room, and apparently he's in Block A. Which is like directly opposite from where I spent the happiest year of my life.

And then we bond over Gavin & Stacey because I keep quoting it and he's never seen it,

And I end up spending three days in his disgracefully untidy room, and all the hostel is going off their nut and I could not give a flying fuck,

because I fucking love this man to pieces.

I'd started cutting again in a big way in response to horrendous bullying.

I can't even fathom doing it now I have J—.

Maybe it is all you need.

DONE-FOR DEE

He caught me in the day of success,
And leaves in my weeks of distress,
Hiding behind thuggish, cuntfuck spunk merchants,
Judging, growing distant – till a lovely insurgence

Of promises kept, long talks in the fields,
Offering his joints till the smoke gently yields
An awful, wonderful, dangerous admission;
I'm drowning in love, and in superstition.

I love my crooked Toddy Biye with all my crooked heart;
But I wait at the window – the tears scald and start,
And he sinks back from sweetheart to druggy, sad criminal,
While I think of him so fucking much it's subliminal.

I suppose you can't know, if it makes the heart fonder.
I wait for the day that once more we can wander.

~ April 18, 2016 ~

THE JOYS OF DESTITUTION

Had a fabbio weekend back in the city I grew up in with my lovely brother and his decent coffee.

Central heating. Clean carpets. Heroin/vallies/gabbies etc a distant existence away, not an immediate life-fading force. Decent, home cooked food. Comfy leather sofas. Books everywhere. Not having to lock my door and do an inventory of what's been nicked every time I need a wee. LIVVY!!!!!!! I cried, obviously. Got my wee [feline] familiar back even just for a while.

Civilisation, and its well-contents.

This place has been grim as fuck and hell on earth in some ways. But being thrust into how the other half live... the dire poverty, drugs, theft, intimidation, gang mentality... boredom, loneliness, destitution, drugs, never trusting anyone as far as you can throw them because they'll steal your grandma's food stamps for a hit.

But also... camaraderie. A few decent, loyal friends, who value morals even amongst drug addiction, 28p to their name, and constant betrayals of trust. People living this life through no fault of their own, and the incredible stories, views, mantras, religions... survival of the soul when the world is a bleak, hostile and judgmental cesspool. The 28-year hardened junkie prostitute who uses her last pennies to buy you a 10 bit of pollen and an Easter egg because she held you while you cried the night before.

What people don't realise about homelessness is the

loneliness you feel. Becoming the lumpenproletariat, left out of the revolution, shirked behind an invisible wall of 'us' and 'them.' And even in the Dirtbox, amongst all this chaos... the spunk merchants are sifted down to a few of the most loyal, interesting and selfless friends I have ever had. On my second day, sitting down with A— and N— having a fag made of doubts off the street with an Everyday Value coffee, and just chatting and laughing... I had a little weep. I wasn't alone.

Plus, (vanity warning) as a formally educated girl from an intellectual family – a rarity in the worst homeless hostel in Dundee – I seem to be a rare resource... and I love being able to help. I've taught literacy, given legal advice, medical advice, drug advice, empathy as an ex-alkie... I've dressed enough infected injection sites for a lifetime, and still being able to help and make people feel looked after even in a tiny way is just wonderful.

Pennilessness is oddly freeing. Nice strangers will give you a fag and a chat, and you are so appreciative of being treated like a human being. Appreciating the little things. Loving how water is free, and so is love and loyalty. Exploring the parks and alleys and backstreets and grit with the Educated Delinquents, and feeling freer and happier than I have since I was a child. Falling irrevocably in love and getting my heartbroken by a Toddy Biye spunk merchant, whose eyes gleam with opportunity, vitality, adventure, and the general feeling that things are going to be OK, no matter what. Fortune is smiling. God is handing out lollies. The only way from here is up.

Plus, learning to defend yourself. Learning to sniff out

bullshit. Learning how to stand up for myself. Learning how to not get your cunt kicked in. Toughening up. Growing a skin thick enough to traverse the insanity.

I'm coming back to Glasgow to take advantage of the functioning mental health services, and leaving behind the dying, prehistoric Dundonian non-existence of support. And also a fresh start, away from copious beefs and dark memories. I'm buzzing to get amongst the Weegie destitute, and see what differences there are.

It's been the most formative experience of my life.

I am so glad everything went to shit. I am gonna write a fucking EPIC play about it all. With the tiny bit of tenacity that mental illness didn't obliterate after all... Hope has sprung once more. Life is what you make of it. But I never want a doubt rollie ever again!

ACKNOWLEDGEMENTS

Since this is Sophie's book, I was reluctant at first to include an acknowledgements page. However, throughout the process of compiling, editing and publishing *Tigerish Waters* for Sophie, I have been struck so consistently by the earnest and often instinctive desire, of so many whom I approached, to offer their time and their professional expertise to help and to advise.

It will remain a source of sadness, that Sophie can't be around to see and to appreciate all of these people who have had faith in her voice – but to all of these people, without whom I could not have made this book what it is, I must express my own gratitude. There are more than I have space here to name, but every contribution will remain deeply appreciated.

I am grateful, first and most particularly, to Katherine McCudden, for the many hours she has spent helping me raise awareness for the book.

To all of those who provided early readings of the text, with encouragements, with incisive appraisals, and with advice – Joe Mulholland, Carl MacDougall, Magi Gibson, Andrew McNeillie, Scott Hames, Patrick Hayes, Callum Lawson, Rowland Bagnall, Adam Heardman and Caitlin Brennan, in particular – I owe a debt which is the more profound, because I know they could never exact it.

Final and special appreciations are reserved for my brother, Tom, and for my parents, Kate and Tim. Without them I can scarcely think how either the production of the book or the surrounding grief could have been navigable.

S. R.

PRAISE FOR *TIGERISH WATERS*

'This writing is riddled with honesty, with a delight in what most people take for granted and a continual attempt to communicate the difficulties of survival. That she succeeds – and the measure of her success – simply magnifies the loss.'

Carl MacDougall, *writer* (Someone Always Robs the Poor, *Freight Books, 2017*), *President of Scottish PEN.*

'Sophie Reilly was already at twenty-one an extraordinarily assured writer, her eye sharp and unflinching, her ear for Scottish demotic unerring. In a flash of genius, the work she has left us becomes greeting and farewell in one, her personal tragedy now Scotland's too to share.'

Andrew McNeillie, *poet* (Winter Moorings, *Carcanet, 2014*), *founder of Archipelago magazine and Clutag Press.*

'Sophie Reilly's writing is powerful. A vivid cocktail of pain, honesty, intelligence and humour. But what shines through most of all is Sophie's humanity, her compassion. These are extraordinarily insightful pieces from a hugely talented young writer we have lost way too soon.'

Magi Gibson, *poet* (Washing Hugh MacDiarmid's Socks, *Luath Press, 2017*).

'Sophie's voice rings out in these pages through her characters, achingly true vignettes of broken and lost souls searching for some kind of way out. Truly remarkable pieces of writing.'

Frank Turner, *singer/songwriter, winner of Kerrang! No Half Measures Award (2010) & 2 Association of Independent Musicians Awards (2011).*

'The real dark thing and no mistake, like a sweet chaotic cousin of *The Trick Is To Keep Breathing*.'

Dr Scott Hames, *Lecturer in Scottish Literature, University of Stirling.*

'This collection is not only the moving record of a young woman's struggle with mental illness, but evidence of a lucid, resourceful, and often witty literary imagination taking shape.'

Professor Patrick Hayes, *Tutorial Fellow of English Literature, St John's College, University of Oxford.*